DINOSAURS

COLOURING BOOK

Published by

Grandreams Limited.
Jadwin House, 205/211 Kentish Town Road, London, NW5 2JU.

Printed in Hungary.
93 – 6945
DS1–2

ALLOSAURUS

STEGOSAURUS

CERATOSAURUS

PACHYCEPHALOSAURS

DILOPHOSAURS

TYRANNOSAURUS

ORNITHOLESTES

SEGNOSAUR

STRUTHIOMIMUS

STEGOSAURUS

STYLACOSAURUS

OUIRAPTOR

VELOCIRAPTOR

OUIRAPTOR

IGUANODON

DEINONYCHUS

TENONTOSAURUS

CHASMOSAURUS

PENTACERATOPS

STEGOSAURUS

ANATOSAURUS

VALCANODON

ALLOSAURUS

SALTASAURUS

SALTASAURUS

PINACOSAURUS

AUIMIMUS

MUTTABURRASAURUS

PROTOCERATOPS

CENTROSAURUS

SAURORNITHOIDES